Fun for ALL!™

Search & Find

by Tony Tallarico

Visit us at www.kidsbooks.com/answers *for the answers.*

SEARCH & FIND® AT THE AIRPORT

- Binoculars
- Birdcage
- Chair
- Clothespins (6)
- Flying bat
- Guardhouse
- Harpoon
- Helicopters (2)
- Hot-air balloon
- Hot dog
- Kite
- Laundry line
- Lost wallet
- Manhole
- Paint rollers (2)
- Paper airplanes (3)
- Parachute
- Pear
- "Pequod"
- Pizza

SEARCH & FIND®
ON THE
FARM

- Boat
- Cactus
- Cave
- Clouds (3)
- "Container Farm"
- Covered wagon
- Donkey
- "Don't Stop" sign
- Elephant
- Ghost
- Giant pumpkin
- "Grade A"
- Kite
- Log pile
- Net
- Periscope
- Pitchfork
- Prisoner
- Scarecrows (5)
- Scuba diver

SEARCH & FIND® AT THE BEACH

- Broom
- Castle
- Cow
- Cruise ship
- Diving board
- Flying fish (4)
- Hearts (3)
- Horse
- Kite
- Litter bug
- Lunch box
- Merman
- Motorcycle
- Mummy
- Sailors (4)
- Sea horse
- Sea serpent
- Starfish (9)
- Stingray
- Submarine